Make it easy...

English

Quick Tests

Age 10–11

Louis Fidge

Test 1 Unstressed vowels

Some **vowels** in longer words are **not stressed** and are difficult to hear.

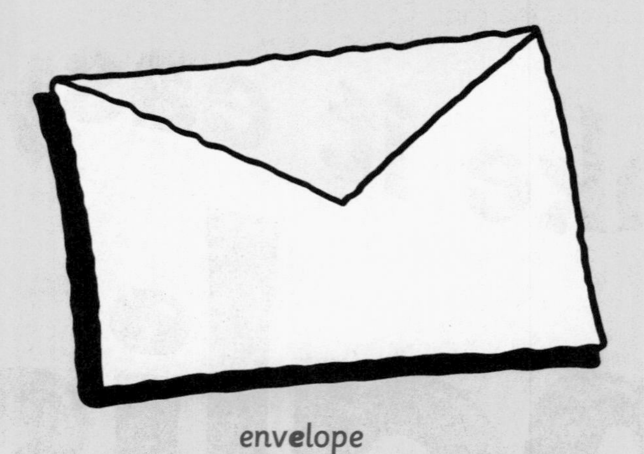

envelope

Fill in the missing vowels.

1. di____mond
2. accident____l
3. entr____nce
4. diff____rent
5. deod____rant
6. myst____ry
7. cru____l
8. int____resting
9. eff____rt
10. monast____ry
11. lunch____on
12. sep____rate
13. butt____n
14. skel____ton
15. ph____tographer

Colour in your score

Test 2 Root words

A **root word** is a word to which **prefixes** or **suffixes** may be added. Sometimes the root word is **easy** to see. Sometimes the root word is **harder** to work out.

bicycle (root word = cycle) beautiful (root word = beauty)

Work out the root word for each of these words.

1. befriend ____________________
2. assistance ____________________
3. centimetre ____________________
4. disability ____________________
5. beggar ____________________
6. engineer ____________________
7. exchange ____________________
8. kingdom ____________________
9. brightness ____________________
10. imperfect ____________________
11. prefix ____________________
12. service ____________________
13. superman ____________________
14. duckling ____________________
15. withhold ____________________

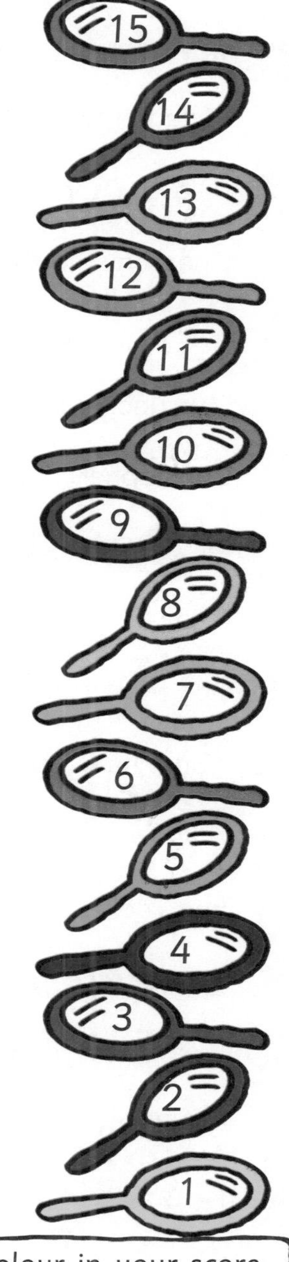

Colour in your score

Test 3 Dashes

A **dash** holds words apart. It is stronger than a comma but is not as strong as a full stop.

I have got a new bike – a mountain bike.

Decide where to put the dash in each sentence.

1. I had my favourite meal spaghetti.
2. I love apples Ben hates them!
3. One boy looked strange he was wearing a mask.
4. I won a prize for coming first in spelling.
5. My uncle appeared laughing as usual.
6. Christopher Wren built a famous cathedral St Paul's.
7. Mr Smith has a sports car a silver one.
8. I love music especially pop music.
9. On the sand I found something interesting an old chest.
10. Work hard or you will never get a good job!
11. I know someone very brave my friend Sarah.
12. Tom collects insects especially beetles.
13. Mount Pico is in the Azores a group of islands.
14. I saw a good programme last night a monster film.
15. My room overlooks a wood a small dark wood.

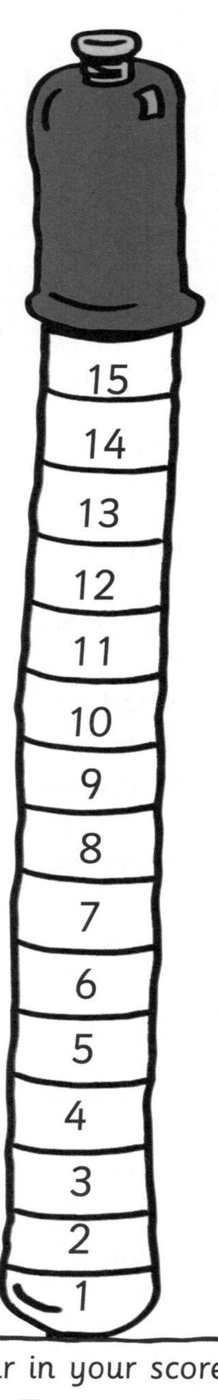

Colour in your score

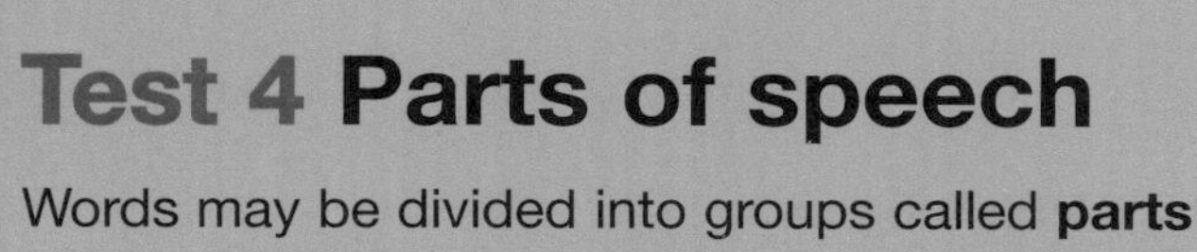

Test 4 Parts of speech

Words may be divided into groups called **parts of speech**. Three important parts of speech are **nouns**, **verbs** and **adjectives**.

This is a **noun**. It is a **naming** word.

The sad baby was crying.

This is an **adjective**. It is a **describing** word. It tells us more about the **noun**.

This is a **verb**. It is a word that describes **actions**.

Underline the noun in each sentence.

1. The red door was shut.
2. The poor old man had to sit down.
3. The wind howled and howled.
4. Some silly children were giggling.
5. My new car was metallic silver.

Underline the verb in each sentence.

6. On Mondays I always ride my bike.
7. Yesterday I ate fifteen biscuits!
8. Next week I will try much harder.
9. Mrs Baker cooked a lovely casserole.
10. Cross the road carefully.

Underline the adjective in each sentence.

11. The floor was slippery.
12. The rough sea crashed against the cliffs.
13. Some colourful birds landed in the garden.
14. In the forest it is scary.
15. My favourite uncle came to see me.

Test 5 Connectives

We sometimes join two **clauses** together by using a **connective**.

I like the summer — *because* — *I go on holiday then.*

clause 1 — connective — clause 2

Choose the best connective to join each pair of clauses.

1. He was not tired ____________ he had to go to bed. (nevertheless/and)
2. I couldn't decide whether to go ____________ stay. (and/or)
3. She put up her umbrella ____________ it was raining. (so that/because)
4. We stopped for a cup of tea ____________ we were early. (as/so)
5. I ate my lunch ____________ I went out. (because/before)
6. The cat chased the birds ____________ they landed. (since/when)
7. I turned up the radio ____________ I could hear it. (as/so that)
8. I won't go out ____________ it is raining. (and/if)
9. If you are late ____________ you will get into trouble. (when/then)
10. I had a wash ____________ I went to the party. (in case/until)
11. I shouted ____________ someone heard me. (until/because)
12. I could not do it ____________ hard I tried. (however/in case)
13. I don't like cheese ____________ my mum does. (and/but)
14. We went home ____________ the match finished. (as soon as/until)
15. We ran fast ____________ we were late. (after/because)

Test 6 Prefixes and suffixes

We add **prefixes** and **suffixes** to words to **change their meanings**.

*accurate – **in**accurate*

A **prefix** is added to the **beginning** of a word. It does **not** change the spelling of the root word.

*happy – happi**ness***

A **suffix** is added to the **end** of a word. It may **sometimes** change the spelling of the root word.

Choose the correct prefix to complete each word.

1. _____graph (ex/auto)
2. _____legal (im/il)
3. _____port (de/mal)
4. _____patient (in/im)
5. _____approve (for/dis)
6. _____behave (dis/mis)
7. _____bark (em/en)
8. _____arrange (pre/pro)

Add the suffix to each root word.
Write the word you make.

9. confide (ence) ______________________
10. bake (ery) ______________________
11. communicate (ion) ______________________
12. study (ent) ______________________
13. replace (ment) ______________________
14. serve (ice) ______________________
15. friendly (ness) ______________________

15 14 13 12 11 10 9 8 7 6 5 4 3 2 1

Colour in your score

Test 7 Active and passive verbs

The footballer kicked the ball.

A verb is **active** when the subject of the sentence does the action.

The ball was kicked by the footballer.

A verb is **passive** when the subject of the sentence has the action done to it.

Decide if the verb in each sentence is active or passive.

1. The child wrote a story. __________
2. The books were written by the author. __________
3. The man rode his mountain bike. __________
4. The telephone was answered by the lady. __________
5. The shoes were worn by Sarah. __________
6. The squirrel climbed the tree. __________
7. The lion chased the antelope. __________
8. The cakes were eaten by Mrs Sallis. __________
9. I received a present yesterday. __________
10. The sword was waved by the pirate. __________
11. The farmer collected the eggs. __________
12. The snake slid along the ground. __________
13. The nest was made by the bird. __________
14. The song was sung by the pop singer. __________
15. I telephoned my friend. __________

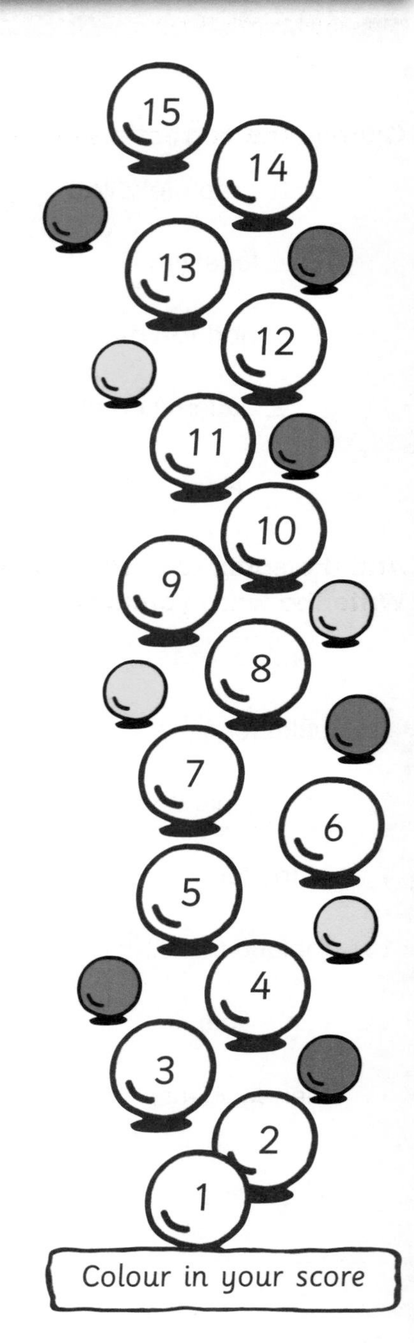

Test 8 Where do our words come from?

English is not just **one language.** It is made up of words taken from many **other languages.**

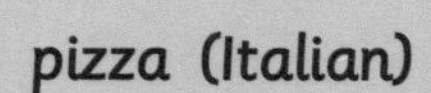

pizza (Italian) yacht (Dutch) vase (French)

Find the words we have borrowed from other languages.

ballerina	skipper	buffet	piano	cabaret
bracket	spaghetti	sketch	schooner	bouquet
opera	confetti	smuggle	landscape	duvet

The words from Italy all end in a vowel other than **e**.

1. ________ 2. ________ 3. ________

4. ________ 5. ________

The words from France all end in **et**.

6. ________ 7. ________ 8. ________

9. ________ 10. ________

The other words are all Dutch words.

11. ________ 12. ________ 13. ________

14. ________ 15. ________

15 14 13 12 11 10 9 8 7 6 5 4 3 2 1

Colour in your score

Test 9 Mnemonics

A **mnemonic** is a way of remembering the spelling of tricky words.

ambitious	believe	business	breadth
cereal	chocolate	conscience	government
island	knowledge	mathematics	
piece	separate	soldier	whole

Find the word with the following word 'hiding' in it.

1. know ____________
2. lie ____________
3. them ____________
4. pie ____________
5. bit ____________
6. late ____________
7. bus ____________
8. men ____________
9. rat ____________
10. bread ____________
11. science ____________
12. who ____________
13. is ____________
14. real ____________
15. die ____________

Test 10 Punctuation

Punctuation marks help us **make sense** of what we read. Where we put punctuation marks can make a difference!

I wore a hat. On my head I wore some boots.

I wore a hat on my head. I wore some boots.

Fill in the missing punctuation marks.

1. Dr Turner___s car was green.
2. Mrs Brown, who was getting angry___ shouted loudly.
3. “Don___t cross the busy road,” Mrs Smith warned Tom.
4. Do you like oranges or lemons best___
5. During the night___ it rained heavily.
6. “Where’s my dinner?___ the giant roared.
7. “I hate sprouts___” Sam shouted.
8. My brother hates music___ but I love it.
9. In my pocket I had a coin, a sweet___ a tissue and a badge.
10. The teachers___ room is next to the office.
11. Where are you going___
12. I___m nearly eleven.
13. The film doesn___t begin for an hour.
14. “Hands up___” the robber shouted.
15. ___My job can be dangerous,” the police officer said.

Test 11 Word origins

The English language has been influenced by **many other languages**. Understanding the **origins** of words sometimes helps us to spell them.

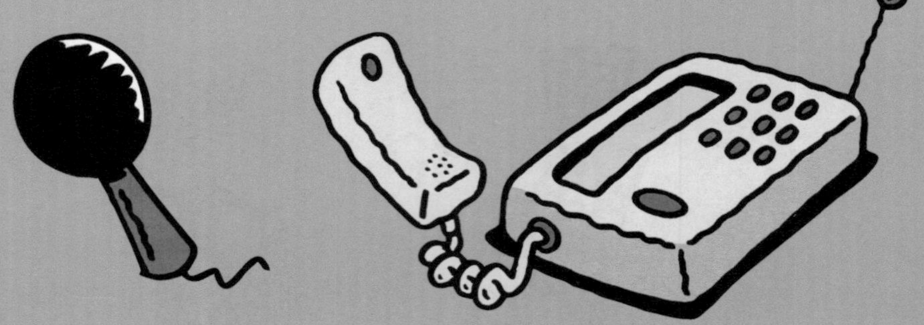

The word **phone** comes from a Greek word meaning **sound**.

micro**phone** tele**phone**

spectator	liberty	signal	liberal	spectacles
audience	liberate	audible	script	signature
describe	scribble	spectacular	auditorium	design

Write some English words we get from these Latin words.

signum (meaning a sign)

1. ________ 2. ________ 3. ________

liber (meaning free)

4. ________ 5. ________ 6. ________

audio (meaning I hear)

7. ________ 8. ________ 9. ________

scribo (meaning I write)

10. ________ 11. ________ 12. ________

specto (meaning I watch)

13. ________ 14. ________ 15. ________

15 14 13 12 11 10 9 8 7 6 5 4 3 2 1

Colour in your score

Test 12 Complex sentences

A **clause** is a **group of words** which can be used as a **whole sentence** or as **part of a sentence**. Many sentences contain **more than one** clause.

This sentence contains two clauses.

The stars twinkled and *the moon shone.*

clause 1 clause 2

Write and say how many clauses there are in each sentence. (1 or 2)

1. I like West Highland Terrier dogs. ________
2. Some cats stay out all night. ________
3. I fell over while we were playing. ________
4. The cat chased the birds that landed on the grass. ________
5. I posted the letter in the post box. ________
6. I bought the comic from the shop. ________
7. When the wind blew the trees swayed. ________
8. Last night I had stomach ache after I ate my tea. ________
9. Cows moo but don't bark. ________
10. Nelson's Column stands in the middle of London. ________
11. The man got stuck when the lift doors closed. ________
12. I went to Spain and visited Madrid. ________
13. My budgie escaped when I left its cage open. ________
14. The lady paid for her hat and left the shop. ________
15. The ugly troll waited patiently under the bridge. ________

Test 13 Proverbs

A **proverb** is a **wise saying** that has been around for a **long time**.

Don't count your chickens before they're hatched.

Match up the beginning and ending of each proverb.

1. Absence makes the heart	than words.
2. Beggars can't be	twice shy.
3. Actions speak louder	never.
4. Birds of a feather	less speed.
5. Once bitten,	choosers.
6. Every cloud has	out of mind.
7. Too many cooks	you leap.
8. Don't put all your eggs	grow fonder.
9. More haste,	than one.
10. Make hay while	flock together.
11. Two heads are better	a silver lining.
12. Better late than	in one basket.
13. Look before	the sun shines.
14. Out of sight,	saves nine.
15. A stitch in time	spoil the broth.

Test 14 Syllables

Words can be broken down into smaller parts, called **syllables**.

um / brel / la (3 syllables)

Think of a suitable second syllable for each word. Write the words you make.

1. de + ____ + mine = ______________________
2. u + ____ + form = ______________________
3. hos + ____ + al = ______________________
4. ex + ____ + lent = ______________________
5. at + ____ + tion = ______________________
6. dif + ____ + ent = ______________________
7. ad + ____ + ture = ______________________
8. syl + ____ + le = ______________________
9. par + ____ + chute = ______________________
10. in + ____ + duce = ______________________
11. be + ____ + ning = ______________________
12. e + ____ + tric = ______________________
13. Sep + ____ + ber = ______________________
14. pun + ____ + ment = ______________________
15. fa + ____ + ite = ______________________

Colour in your score

Test 15 Using dictionaries

You can use a **dictionary** to check the **spelling** of words.

~~hippapotamis~~ ~~hippopotomus~~ hippopotamus

Each of the following words is spelt incorrectly.
Write each word correctly. Use a dictionary if necessary.

1. ocasion ______________________
2. priviledge ______________________
3. fasinate ______________________
4. exitement ______________________
5. immidiate ______________________
6. reconise ______________________
7. mathmatics ______________________
8. dissappear ______________________
9. controll ______________________
10. marrage ______________________
11. rubarb ______________________
12. temporey ______________________
13. disasterous ______________________
14. sissors ______________________
15. enviroment ______________________

Test 16 Spelling rules

Some **spelling rules** are helpful to remember. One common rule is: **i** (when it makes the sound **ee**) before **e** except after **c**.

Follow the rule. Choose ie or ei to complete each word.

1. bel_____ve
2. rec_____ve
3. c_____ling
4. ch_____f
5. p_____ce
6. rel_____f
7. f_____ld
8. perc_____ve
9. dec_____ve
10. dec_____t
11. lad_____s
12. pr_____st
13. n_____ce
14. f_____rce
15. conc_____t

Test 17 Conditionals

A **conditional verb** tells you the action **might** happen (or might have happened), because it **depends** on someone or something else.

*I **would** buy an ice-cream if I had any money.*

Say if the conditional verbs in bold indicate the past or future tense.

1. If it stops raining we **might go** out. ____________
2. If I had searched I **would have found** my watch. ____________
3. She **would have passed** her test if she had tried harder. ____________
4. I **might go** to America next year. ____________
5. If I had heard the alarm I **would have got** up. ____________
6. I **could have saved** my money but I didn't. ____________
7. I **might play** cricket tomorrow. ____________
8. If I were in charge I **would give** everyone a holiday. ____________
9. If you won the Lottery what **would** you **buy**? ____________
10. I **could have won** the race if I hadn't fallen over. ____________
11. I **should have left** while I had the chance. ____________
12. No one **would notice** if you went later. ____________
13. How much **would** it **cost** to buy that dress? ____________
14. I **would have read** the book if you hadn't disturbed me. ____________
15. If you come to town with me I **might buy** you a present. ____________

Test 18 Shortening words

When we write notes we can **abbreviate** some words.

I come from the USA.

USA = United States of America

Match up each abbreviation with its meaning.

1.	kph	United Nations
2.	dept	note well
3.	PTO	Crescent
4.	UN	kilometres per hour
5.	Rd	Her (or His) Royal Highness
6.	anon	please reply
7.	etc	Member of Parliament
8.	NB	department
9.	RSVP	Road
10.	BC	please turn over
11.	Sq	Before Christ
12.	Cresc	United Kingdom
13.	MP	anonymous
14.	UK	Square
15.	HRH	etcetera

Test 19 Our changing language

Our language is **changing** all the time. Words **fall out of use** and **new words** enter our language.

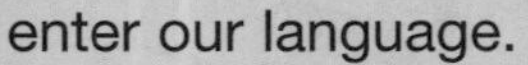

A **cobbler** made shoes.
We no longer use this word much.

An **astronaut** flies in space.
This is a new space-age word.

Match up these old words with their meanings.

1.	frock	hat
2.	quaff	drinking cup
3.	bonnet	dress
4.	satchel	container for coal
5.	guinea	drink
6.	tinker	an old coin
7.	goblet	schoolbag
8.	scuttle	a man who mended pots

Complete these new 'computer' words.

9. mon__ __or
10. m__ __em
11. key__ __ __rd
12. e-m__ __ __
13. __ous__
14. inter__ __ __
15. w__bs__ __ __

Test 20 Formal language

We speak to each other ***informally****.* ***Official language*** *is more* ***formal****.*

Match up the formal words or phrases with their informal meanings.

	Formal	Informal
1.	forename	capital letters
2.	marital status	the work you do
3.	block letters	drinks
4.	nationality	on the back
5.	occupation	first name
6.	I beg your pardon.	No smoking
7.	Entrance forbidden!	whether you are married or single
8.	duplicate	pay
9.	beverages	what country you come from
10.	consume	sorry
11.	on the reverse	eat
12.	remuneration	attach
13.	dwelling	You are not allowed in.
14.	Smoking prohibited!	where you live
15.	append	a copy

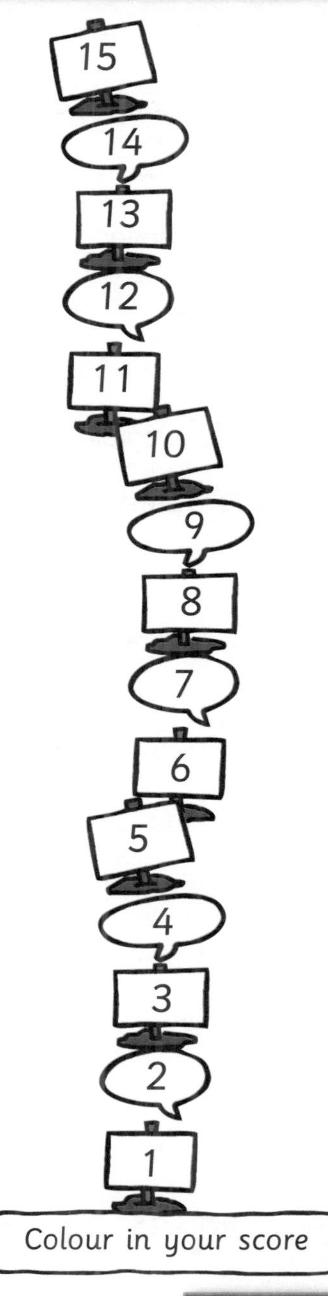

Test 21 Changing words

We can often change a **root word** by adding a **prefix**.

We can often change a **root word** by adding a **suffix**.

discomfort ← *comfort* → *comfortable*

(root word + prefix) (root word) (root word + suffix)

Choose the correct prefix to complete each word.

1. _____board (a/be)
2. _____loved (a/be)
3. _____mature (in/im)
4. _____considerate (in/im)
5. _____legible (ir/il)
6. _____responsible (ir/il)
7. _____noculars (bi/tri)
8. _____dent (bi/tri)

Work out the root word of each of these words.

9. accidentally ________________
10. clumsily ________________
11. suspicious ________________
12. angry ________________
13. circular ________________
14. metallic ________________
15. sensible ________________

Test 22 More about complex sentences

A **complex sentence** contains a **main clause** and a **subordinate** (less important) **clause**. The subordinate clause may not make sense on its own.

The detective arrested the man *who had robbed the bank.*

main clause subordinate clause

Join up each main clause with a sensible subordinate clause.

Main clause	Subordinate clause
1. The children started talking	although I watered them.
2. Tom's mum was cross	because the gate was open.
3. The flowers did not grow	where I saw huge skyscrapers.
4. I visited New York	when the teacher went out.
5. The dog escaped	which I had lost.
6. It often rains	when she saw his messy bedroom.
7. I found the key	so I always carry an umbrella.

Now try these.

Main clause	Subordinate clause
8. I had a bath	before she left.
9. The audience cheered	because it was starving.
10. My aunt hugged me	who is very naughty.
11. The lady asked the way	because I was so muddy.
12. Abdi is the boy	when she got lost.
13. Mrs Cane won the Lottery	before it got dark.
14. The child ran home	when the band played.
15. The dog ate hungrily	so she bought a new house.

Test 23 Phrases and clauses

A **clause** may be used either as a **whole sentence** or as **part of a sentence**. A clause always contains a verb.

A **phrase** does **not** contain a **verb**. A phrase does **not make sense** on its own.

The balloon popped — clause

with a loud bang. — phrase

Write whether each of these is a clause or a phrase.

1. Sarah slipped over. ____________
2. in a muddy puddle ____________
3. after the programme ____________
4. Sam rode her bike. ____________
5. The spacecraft landed on the hill. ____________
6. as fast as a flash ____________
7. The lady put down her bag. ____________
8. until next time ____________
9. The lion pounced on the gazelle. ____________
10. near the lake ____________
11. until midnight ____________
12. The baby smiled at me. ____________
13. Some cars have big boots. ____________
14. all green and slimy ____________
15. A giraffe has a long neck. ____________

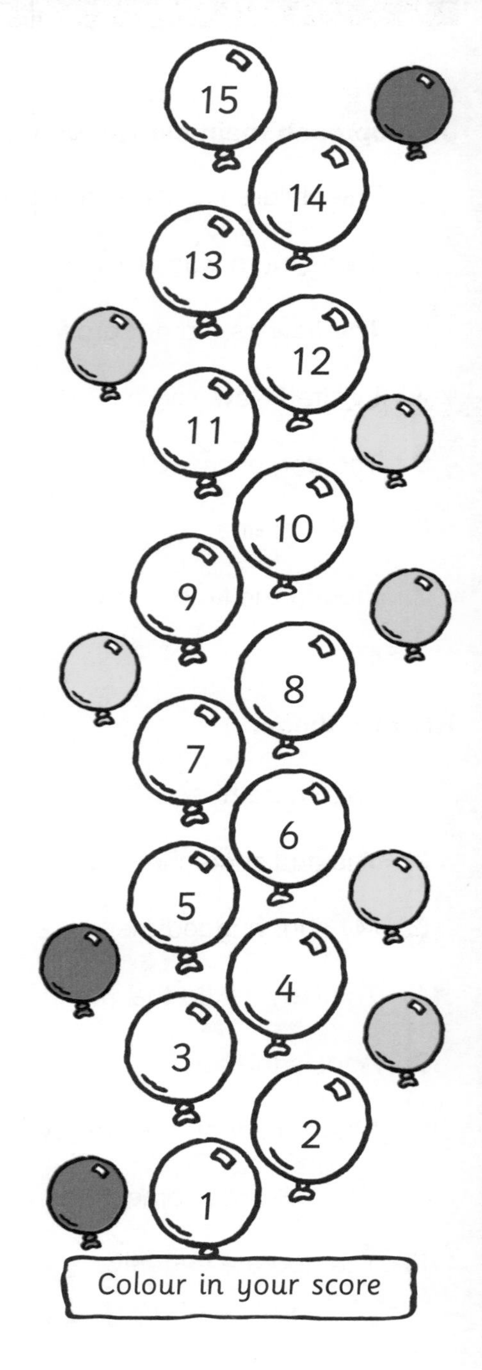

Test 24 More punctuation

It is important to check that your **punctuation** is correct.

Fill in the missing punctuation marks.

1. The monkeys were playing in the tree___
2. Amir bought eggs___ milk, bread and flour at the shop.
3. "Where do you live___" she asked.
4. "Get out___" he shouted.
5. The dog___s tail was wagging.
6. ___What book are you reading?" Shiraz asked.
7. After tea___ Mark watched TV.
8. Mrs Best said___ "Where is my bag?"
9. It isn___t a nice day.
10. The toy didn___t cost much.
11. "Come with me___ Ben," the teacher said.
12. "Stop that at once___" Mr Khan demanded.
13. The dog, a small poodle___ yapped loudly.
14. The door was open___ inviting him to enter.
15. "When I___ve got enough money, I'll retire," Mr Farr said.

Test 25 Another spelling rule

When a word has one vowel before a single final consonant, we double the consonant before adding a **suffix** – if the last syllable is stressed.

begin – beginning

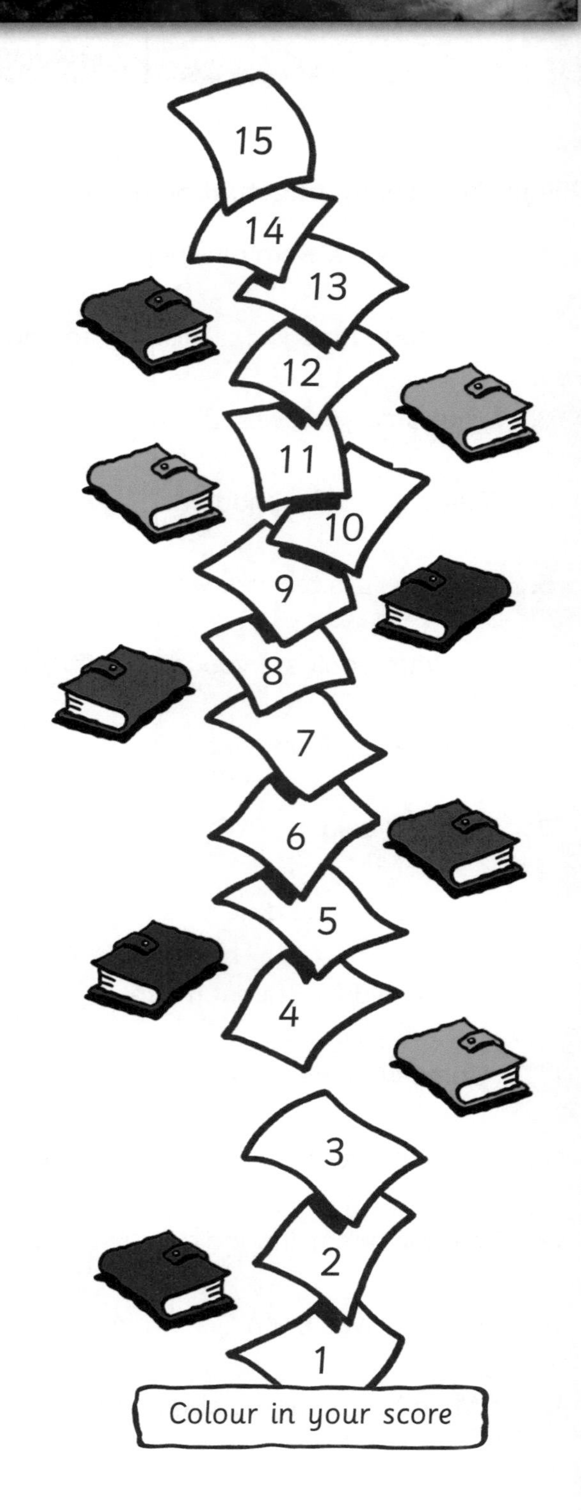

Add the suffix ing. Write the word you make.

1. rebel ________________
2. admit ________________
3. forget ________________
4. prefer ________________
5. signal ________________

Add the suffix ed. Write the word you make.

6. regret ________________
7. transmit ________________
8. travel ________________
9. occur ________________
10. control ________________

Take the suffix off. Write the root word you are left with.

11. fulfilled ________________
12. forbidding ________________
13. referred ________________
14. marvelled ________________
15. omitting ________________

Test 26 Long and short vowels

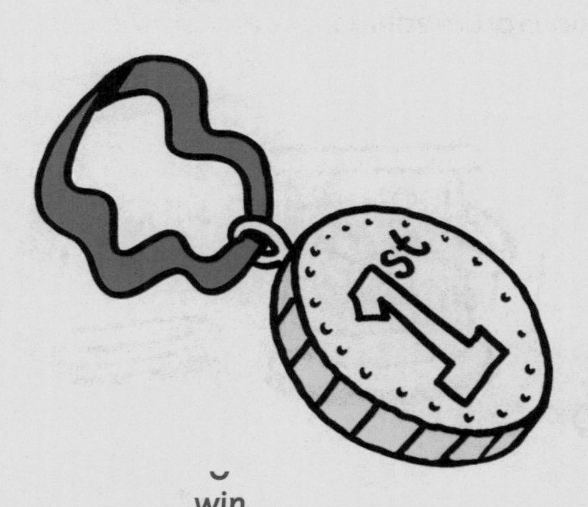

$\breve{\text{win}}$ — win

Short vowels make the **sound** of the letter.

$\bar{\text{wine}}$ — wine

Long vowels say the **name** of the letter.

Use the signs to show whether the vowels are long ¯ or short ˘ .

1. sigh
2. plush
3. truth
4. wild
5. swam
6. desk
7. show
8. shy
9. flip
10. drip
11. text
12. stay
13. most
14. blind
15. lost

Test 27 Common word endings

It is helpful to learn the spelling of **common word endings**.

Choose our or ure to complete each word.

1. flav__________
2. cult__________
3. furnit__________
4. fav__________
5. mixt__________
6. hon__________
7. vap__________
8. inj__________
9. lab__________
10. col__________
11. fig__________
12. fail__________
13. vig__________
14. harb__________
15. capt__________

Test 28 More common word endings

It is helpful to learn the spelling of **common word endings**.

CHEM LAB inc.

nurs**ery** laborat**ory** di**ary**

Each of these words is spelt incorrectly. Spell each word correctly.

1. machinary ____________________
2. factery ____________________
3. delivory ____________________
4. dictionery ____________________
5. observatery ____________________
6. discovary ____________________
7. granery ____________________
8. laboratary ____________________
9. jewellory ____________________
10. dormitery ____________________
11. flattary ____________________
12. estuory ____________________
13. militery ____________________
14. territery ____________________
15. librory ____________________

Test 29 Similes

A **simile** is when one thing is compared to another. We often use the word **as** in similes.

The children were **as** quiet **as** mice.

Complete these well-known similes with these words.

tortoise	swan	bat	fox	ox	mule	lion	elephant

1. as blind as a ______________
2. as obstinate as a ______________
3. as crafty as a ______________
4. as heavy as an ______________
5. as fierce as a ______________
6. as strong as an ______________
7. as graceful as a ______________
8. as slow as a ______________

Now do these.

thin	regular	fit	easy	safe	flat	sour

9. as ____________ as a fiddle
10. as ____________ as vinegar
11. as ____________ as a pancake
12. as ____________ as a rake
13. as ____________ as clockwork
14. as ____________ as ABC
15. as ____________ as a bank

15 14 13 12 11 10 9 8 7 6 5 4 3 2 1

Colour in your score

Test 30 Word games

We can learn a lot by playing **word games**. They can help us with our **spelling** and help to **improve our vocabulary**.

Use a dictionary to help you work out these clues.

These words all begin with she.

1. a law officer ____________
2. a place for protection ____________
3. very steep ____________
4. large scissors ____________

These words all begin with go.

5. a hairy berry ____________
6. a prickly shrub ____________
7. glasses for protection ____________
8. a young goose ____________

These words all begin with pea.

9. quiet ____________
10. a bird with beautiful feathers ____________
11. a kind of fuel ____________
12. grows in a pod underground ____________

These words all begin with ant.

13. old and valuable ____________
14. an animal like a deer ____________
15. kind of aerial ____________

15 14 13 12 11 10 9 8 7 6 5 4 3 2 1

Colour in your score

ANSWERS

Test 1
The missing vowels are in **bold**.

1. di**a**mond
2. accident**a**l
3. entr**a**nce
4. diff**e**rent
5. deod**o**rant
6. myst**e**ry
7. cru**e**l
8. int**e**resting
9. eff**o**rt
10. monast**e**ry
11. lunch**e**on
12. sep**a**rate
13. butt**o**n
14. skel**e**ton
15. ph**o**tographer

Test 2
1. friend
2. assist
3. metre
4. able
5. beg
6. engine
7. change
8. king
9. bright
10. perfect
11. fix
12. serve
13. man
14. duck
15. hold

Test 3
1. I had my favourite meal – spaghetti.
2. I love apples – Ben hates them!
3. One boy looked strange – he was wearing a mask.
4. I won a prize – for coming first in spelling.
5. My uncle appeared – laughing as usual.
6. Christopher Wren built a famous cathedral – St Paul's.
7. Mr Smith has a sports car – a silver one.
8. I love music – especially pop music.
9. On the sand I found something interesting – an old chest.
10. Work hard – or you will never get a good job!
11. I know someone very brave – my friend Sarah.
12. Tom collects insects – especially beetles.
13. Mount Pico is in the Azores – a group of islands.
14. I saw a good programme last night – a monster film.
15. My room overlooks a wood – a small dark wood.

Test 4
1. door
2. man
3. wind
4. children
5. car
6. ride
7. ate
8. will try
9. cooked
10. cross
11. slippery
12. rough
13. colourful
14. scary
15. favourite

Test 5
1. nevertheless
2. or
3. because
4. as
5. before
6. when
7. so that
8. if
9. then
10. in case
11. until
12. however
13. but
14. as soon as
15. because

Test 6
Answers 1–8: the correct prefix is in **bold**.

1. **auto**graph
2. **il**legal
3. **de**port
4. **im**patient
5. **dis**approve
6. **mis**behave
7. **em**bark
8. **pre**arrange
9. confidence
10. bakery
11. communication
12. student
13. replacement
14. service
15. friendliness

Test 7
1. active
2. passive
3. active
4. passive
5. passive
6. active
7. active
8. passive
9. active
10. passive
11. active
12. active
13. passive
14. passive
15. active

Test 8
1. ballerina
2. piano
3. spaghetti
4. opera
5. confetti
6. buffet
7. cabaret
8. bracket
9. bouquet
10. duvet
11. skipper
12. sketch
13. schooner
14. smuggle
15. landscape

Test 9
1. knowledge
2. believe
3. mathematics
4. piece
5. ambitious
6. chocolate
7. business
8. government
9. separate
10. breadth
11. conscience
12. whole
13. island
14. cereal
15. soldier

Test 10
The missing punctuation marks are in **bold**.

1. Dr Turner's car was green.
2. Mrs Brown, who was getting angry**,** shouted loudly.
3. "Don't cross the busy road," Mrs Smith warned Tom.
4. Do you like oranges or lemons best**?**
5. During the night**,** it rained heavily.
6. "Where's my dinner?" the giant roared.
7. "I hate sprouts!" Sam shouted.
8. My brother hates music – but I love it.
9. In my pocket I had a coin, a sweet**,** a tissue and a badge.
10. The teachers' room is next to the office.
11. Where are you going**?**
12. I'm nearly eleven.
13. The film doesn't begin for an hour.
14. "Hands up!" the robber shouted.
15. "My job can be dangerous," the police officer said.

Test 11
1. signal
2. signature
3. design
4. liberty
5. liberal
6. liberate
7. audience
8. audible
9. auditorium
10. script
11. describe
12. scribble
13. spectator
14. spectacles
15. spectacular

Test 12
1. 1
2. 1
3. 2
4. 2
5. 1
6. 1
7. 2
8. 2
9. 2
10. 1
11. 2
12. 2
13. 2
14. 2
15. 1

Test 13
1. grow fonder
2. choosers
3. than words
4. flock together
5. twice shy
6. a silver lining
7. spoil the broth
8. in one basket
9. less speed
10. the sun shines
11. than one
12. never
13. you leap
14. out of mind
15. saves nine

Test 14
The missing second syllable is in **bold**.

1. de**ter**mine
2. u**ni**form
3. hos**pit**al
4. ex**cel**lent
5. at**ten**tion
6. dif**fer**ent
7. ad**ven**ture
8. syl**lab**le
9. par**a**chute
10. in**tro**duce
11. be**gin**ning
12. e**lec**tric
13. Sep**tem**ber
14. pun**ish**ment
15. fa**vour**ite

Test 15
1. occasion
2. privilege
3. fascinate
4. excitement
5. immediate
6. recognise
7. mathematics
8. disappear
9. control
10. marriage
11. rhubarb
12. temporary
13. disastrous
14. scissors
15. environment